CW00558513

nails

nails

WITH NAIL ART BY

PANSY ALEXANDER

AT NAILS TO GO

KYLE CATHIE LIMITED

First published in Great Britain in 1997 by

Kyle Cathie Limited
20 Vauxhall Bridge Road
London SW1V 2SA

ISBN 1 85626 292 8

Text © 1997 **Kyle Cathie Limited**
Photography © 1997 **Laura Hodgson**
Designed by **Button Design Company**
Nail art by **Pansy Alexander** at **Nails to Go**

Kyle Cathie Limited is hereby identified as the author of this work in accordance
with Section 77 of the Copyright, Designs and Patents Act 1988.

A CIP catalogue record for this title is available from the British Library.

Printed and bound in Italy by Graphicom srl.

TO LOTTE

WITHOUT WHOM THIS BOOK WOULD

NOT HAVE BEEN MADE

Contents

Contents

Introduction

Au naturel

ALWAYS KEEP YOUR NAILS WELL MANICURED

Nail care

Always use the pads of your fingers, not your nails, when touching things. • TREAT YOUR CUTICLES WITH NOURISHING CREAM AND PUSH THEM BACK ONCE A WEEK WITH A COTTON WOOL-COVERED ORANGE STICK. WEAR PROTECTIVE GLOVES WHEN YOU ARE USING HARSH CLEANING PRODUCTS, ALWAYS DRY YOUR HANDS THOROUGHLY AND USE HAND CREAM REGULARLY • Treat soft and broken nails with a nail strengthener applied every other day for 3 to 6 weeks only (completely remove and reapply once a week). Try not to use it too often. • NEVER USE NAIL VARNISH REMOVER MORE THAN ONCE A WEEK AS IT STRIPS THE NAILS. ALWAYS USE A NON-ACETONE SOLUTION.

Regular manicure

You should need to file your nails only once a month. File them into rounded tips, square tips or the popular 'squoval' shape which is half-way between the two. Use a broad and gentle emery board which will not damage your nails. WHEN APPLYING VARNISH ALWAYS USE A BASE COAT THEN TWO COATS OF YOUR CHOSEN COLOUR. 'LIFT' THE NAILS EVERY OTHER DAY WITH A COAT OF YOUR FAVOURITE TOP GLAZE. • If your nails are very short you can have extensions done by a professional. They can last for months if you maintain them but, remember, this is not a cheap option.

Nail art

BEFORE YOU START, MAKE SURE THAT YOU HAVE GOT EVERYTHING YOU NEED. A COLLECTION OF BASIC NAIL GLOSSES IS ESSENTIAL: BLACK, WHITE, GOLD, SILVER, RED, BLUE, GREEN, YELLOW, PINK AND BROWN. YOU MAY ALSO WANT TO GET SOME GLITTER VARNISHES. • Add to your stock as you come across new colours. For large patches of colour use nail varnish and a fine paint brush; for delicate nail art you will need water-based paints and a very fine paint brush, all available from art suppliers. If you want to paint perfect straight lines then use nail striping. Nail piercing must only be done by a professional. • THE SIMPLEST NAIL ART IS DONE USING BOUGHT TRANSFERS AND STENCILS: JUST APPLY YOUR BASE COAT, TWO COATS OF YOUR COLOUR AND, WHEN YOUR VARNISH IS **DRY** (THIS IS VERY IMPORTANT), APPLY THE TRANSFERS OR STENCIL COLOUR, FINISH WITH A COAT OF GLAZE AND… HEY PRESTO! IT IS ALSO VERY EASY (AND CHEAPER) TO MAKE YOUR OWN STENCILS BY CUTTING OUT TINY SHAPES FROM A SHEET OF FLEXIBLE CARD – START WITH SIMPLE SHAPES SUCH AS HEARTS, STARS AND CIRCLES AND MOVE ON WHEN YOU GAIN MORE CONFIDENCE. • For extra sparkle, add rhinestones to your designs; they come in all colours and can be added to your nail with a dot of glaze and then sealed with another coat. You can even cut out tiny pictures from magazines and add them to your designs. The possibilities are endless! Have fun! • SEE PAGE 63 FOR ADVICE ABOUT STOCKISTS.

Daisy Chain

All girls need flower power

WHITE BASE COLOUR

PINK AND YELLOW DAISIES AND GREEN LEAVES PAINTED WITH

FINE PAINTBRUSH

Café au lait

tempting
two-tone

FRENCH MANICURE LOOK: BROWN BASE WITH CREAMY WHITE TIPS

Checkmate

DARE TO BE SQUARE

BLACK BASE COLOUR

SILVER GLOSS STRIPES, USING NAIL STRIPING (SEE PAGE 63)

SILVER GLITTER SQUARES

Leopard Baby

pad around

and paint up

your claws

GOLD BASE COLOUR

BLACK OUTLINES FILLED WITH BROWN PAINT

Shanghai Susie

PUT ON YOUR

CHEONGSAM, BOB

YOUR HAIR AND

FINISH OFF WITH

PERFECT SUSIE WONG

NAIL DESIGNS

BLACK BASE COLOUR

GOLD TRANSFERS (SEE PAGE 63)

GOLD RHINESTONES (SEE PAGE 63)

On the edge

RING THE CHANGES

. . . .

BABY BLUE BASE COLOUR

BLACK NAIL STRIPING

NAIL PIERCING DONE BY PROFESSIONAL NAIL ARTIST

Candy Girl

GIVE YOUR WARDROBE A NEW TWIST WITH GLITTER GOLD STRIPES THAT DEMAND TO BE SEEN

WHITE BASE COLOUR

GOLD DIAGONAL STRIPES PAINTED WITH NAIL STRIPING

GLITTER VARNISH

Violet Child

A sweet
statement
for a
gentle mood

PINK BASE COLOUR WITH LILAC TIP

FLOWERS PAINTED WITH FINE PAINTBRUSH USING VIOLET, YELLOW,

WHITE AND LEAF GREEN

Camouflage

BE READY FOR ARMED COMBAT

BEIGE AND MOSS GREEN BASE COLOUR

KHAKI GREEN, BROWN AND WHITE PATCHES APPLIED WITH FINE

AND MEDIUM PAINTBRUSH

Glitter chick

come on
the .
dancing queen

ASSORTED GLITTER POLISHES

Spot the difference

ITSY BITSY,

TEENY WEENY,

YELLOW POLKA DOT...

SKY BLUE BASE COLOUR

YELLOW POLKA DOTS PAINTED WITH FINE PAINTBRUSH

Burning bright!

FOR
SAVAGE
NIGHTS

WHITE BASE COLOUR

TIGER TRANSFERS (SEE PAGE 63)

Little Feet

Always a step ahead

WHITE BASE COLOUR

BLACK TRANSFERS (SEE PAGE 63)

Fly the flag

THE PRIDE OF THE NATION

....

WHITE BASE COLOUR

RED STRIPES PAINTED USING NAIL STRIPING (SEE PAGE 63)

BLUE TIP WITH WHITE STARS USING FINE PAINTBRUSH

Starlight

GLOW
IN THE
DARK

MIDNIGHT BLUE BASE COLOUR

FLUORESCENT TRANSFER STARS (SEE PAGE 63)

Flower power

let it
grow
on you

YELLOW-GOLD BASE COLOUR

FLOWER PAINTED WITH LEAF GREEN, RED AND ORANGE PAINT,

APPLIED WITH FINE PAINTBRUSH

Pretty in pink

be my
love

BABY PINK BASE COLOUR

PINK HEART PAINTED USING STENCIL (SEE PAGE 63)

PINK RHINESTONES

Yin and yang

PERFECT HARMONY

PERFECT HARMONY

RED BASE COLOUR

SYMBOL PAINTED WITH BLACK AND WHITE PAINT USING
FINE PAINTBRUSH

WHITE AND BLACK RHINESTONES (SEE PAGE 63)

Gender specific

girl *meets* boy

PINK AND BLUE BASE COLOUR

TRANSFERS (SEE PAGE 63)

Mondrian moment

BUT IS IT ART?

IVORY BASE COLOUR

BLACK LINES WITH BLUE, RED AND YELLOW SQUARES

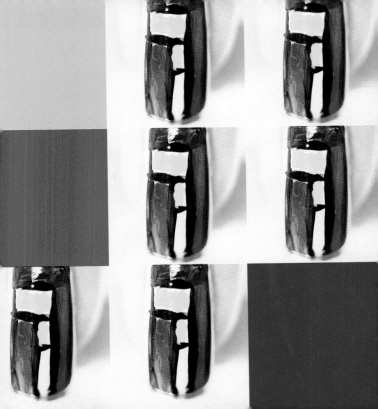

Silver celebration

PARTY
ON

SILVER GLITTER BASE COLOUR

BRIGHT BLUE FIGURES APPLIED WITH FINE PAINTBRUSH

Smiley

DON'T WORRY. BE HAPPY!

YELLOW BASE COLOUR

SMILEY TRANSFER (SEE PAGE 63)

Quarter daughter

KEEP YOURSELF
IN CHECK

....

WHITE BASE COLOUR

BRONZE AND GOLD GLITTER SQUARES PAINTED USING

NAIL STRIPING (SEE PAGE 63)

Card sharp

always let others know your hand

WHITE BASE COLOUR

CARD SYMBOLS PAINTED USING NAIL STENCILS IN BLACK AND RED

(SEE PAGE 63)

Useful information

For professional nail artists and nail supplies look in your local telephone directory under 'Beauty' or try the Internet.

Nail salons will often sell you the transfers, nail striping and rhinestones you need or they can supply you with the addresses of the best mail order companies. Many transfers and nail art stencils are now becoming widely available in gift shops. You can also make your own stencils using a very flexible piece of card and a craft knife.

Water-based paint for your nail designs, and fine art brushes are available at good art suppliers everywhere.

For mail-order nail art supplies and further details contact:

NAILS TO GO, HYPE DF, 48–52 KENSINGTON HIGH STREET, LONDON W8 4PE, UK +44 (0)171 795 6333